mr Bean™

A Day at the Beach

tigeraspect
PRODUCTIONS
an endemol company

Popcorn
ELT
Readers

New Words

boat

It's a **boat**.

beach

They are at the **beach**.

caravan

This is a **caravan**.

cloud

There are three **clouds**.

follow

They are **following** the teacher.

drive

She's **driving**.

people

There are four **people**.

Where's the popcorn?
Look in your book.
Can you find it?

mr Bean™

A Day at the Beach

Mr Bean is going to the **beach**.

Let's go, Teddy!

There are a lot of **people** at the **beach**.

Mr Bean **drives** across the **beach**.

Now there are no **people**.

Mr Bean is happy.

Mr Bean plays on the **beach**.

Mr Bean is happy.

I love the sun!

Now there is a big **caravan** next to Mr Bean.

Where is the sun now?

Mr Bean **drives** his car again.

Now he is happy.

But where is the sun now?

The sun is behind a **cloud**.

Then Mr Bean sees the sun again.

He **follows** the sun.

He **drives** into the town.

The sun is on the road!

Now the sun is behind a **cloud** again.

Mr Bean **drives** out of the town.

Now the sun is in the sea.

Mr Bean sees a **boat**.

Quick, Teddy!

Mr Bean **drives** onto the **boat**.

Now Mr Bean is in the sun again!

THE END

After you read

1 Put the pictures in order. Write 1-5.

a

b

1

c

d

Bob-a-long Ferries

e

2 Find the words.

a

b

c

✓

b	c	p	s	u	n	n
e	a	e	b	o	a	t
a	r	o	w	l	c	e
c	a	p	k	k	l	f
h	v	l	f	e	o	o
i	a	e	q	x	u	g
c	n	r	j	e	d	t

d

f

e

3 **What does Mr Bean do? Complete the sentences with the verbs.**

follows ~~drives~~ sees plays

a) Mr Bean d r i v e s his car.

b) Mr Bean _ _ _ _ _ on the beach.

c) Mr Bean _ _ _ _ _ _ _ the sun.

d) Mr Bean _ _ _ _ a boat.

4 **Draw a picture of Mr Bean.**

Quiz time!

Answer the questions. Yes or No?

Yes　No

1) Mr Bean is going to the beach. ☐ ☐

2) There are a lot of people on the beach. ☐ ☐

3) Mr Bean follows the clouds. ☐ ☐

4) Mr Bean drives on the sea. ☐ ☐

5) Mr Bean finds the sun on a boat. ☐ ☐

SCORES

How many of your answers are correct?

0-2: Read the book again! Can you answer the questions now?

3-4: Good work! You like Mr Bean!

5: Wow! Mr Bean likes you!

23

Chant

1 Listen and read.

Where's the sun?

Where's the sun?
It's on the beach!
Quick, Teddy. Let's go!

Where the sun?
It's behind a cloud!
Quick, Teddy. Let's go!

Where's the sun?
It's in the sea!
Quick, Teddy. Let's go!

Where's the sun?
Here it is!
Ahhhh, we love the sun!

2 Say the chant.